On and Off the Road

Contents

Mountain Biking

Written by
Paul Reeder

Mountain bikes are fun to ride.
They can go through mud and water.

They have strong frames and fat tyres so they can go off the road.

You can ride up mountains
and speed down hills.
You can ride through forests
and on sand.

If something blocks your way, you can ride over it.

Are there good places to ride a mountain bike where you live?

You can even ride mountain bikes on snow!

Some people like to race mountain bikes.
They race over hills.
They race through forests.

They race through mud and water.
Sometimes they CRASH!

Mountain Bike Talk

air – the space between the tyres and the path when you jump

bail – to jump off your bike before you crash

biff – to crash

buzz – the happy feeling you get when you ride

death cookies – the rocks that make your bike wobble

face plant – to fall off your bike and onto your face

jet – to ride very fast

mud dive – to fall into mud when your bike gets stuck

powerslide – to slide sideways on two wheels

roadie – a person who likes to ride on the road

skid lid – a helmet

stack – to crash

steed – a bike

tea party – when people stop to talk and do not want to keep riding

wheelie – when the front wheel comes up off the path

wipe out – to crash

wonky – when something on your bike is broken

zonk – to get tired

Can you think of special words used in other sports?

9

Beach Volleyball

Written by Victoria St John

Photographed by Dean Iversen

"Good shot, Tom!"

Tom plays on a beach volleyball team. His team is very good.

Q. What is beach volleyball?

A. Beach volleyball is a sport that you play on the sand.

You hit a ball over a big net. You must move very fast.

Q. How do you play
beach volleyball?

A. There are two players
on each side of the net.
You try to hit the ball
so the other side can't get it.
You can't hit the net.
You can't hit players
on the other team.

Q. How do you get in shape to play beach volleyball?

A. I run.
I lift weights.

And I play beach volleyball almost every day.

Q. What are your plans for this year?

A. This year I hope to play
beach volleyball very well.
I plan to play beach volleyball
in lots of places.
If I play well, I may get to go
to the Olympic Games.

Good luck, Tom!

Do you like the beach?
Do you like fast games?
If you do, then maybe
you can play
beach volleyball.

The Fun Rally

Written by Paul Reeder   Illustrated by Falcon Halo

Pedro liked to play sports.
He liked races and
he liked to help people.

One day, Pedro read about a fun rally.
"I want to do that," he said.

Pedro went to see his friend, Maria.
"Will you do this fun rally
with me?" he asked.

17

"It will take three weeks.
You race in cars,
on skis,
on bikes,
and in boats.
And you help people,"
he said.

What do you think
Pedro and Maria
took with them
on the fun rally?

"When you win a race
or help someone,
you get points.
The team
with the most points
wins a big prize!"

"Okay, I'll come,"
said Maria.
"It will be fun."

KEY
Driving
Skiing
Biking
Kayaking
Rowing

Santiago

SOUTH AMERICA

Meeting Place 1

Meeting Place 2

Meeting Place 3

Tierra del Fuego

19

START

20

Pedro and Maria entered the rally.
They drove in cars.
They raced on skis,
on bikes,
and in boats.

Along the way,
Pedro and Maria helped people.
They helped to build roads,
to make maps,
and to fix bridges.

Pedro and Maria
helped other rally teams, too.
They made lots of new friends.

One day, Pedro and Maria
came to a small town.
One of the houses had lost
its roof in a big storm.

Pedro and Maria helped to put
a new roof on the house.
People in the town helped, too.

The rally took three weeks.
Finally, Pedro and Maria
got to the finish line.
Lots of people won prizes.
Pedro and Maria
won a prize for helping.

It was fun to drive all the different cars with Maria.

I'm glad Pedro asked me to come on the fun rally.

FINISH

Pedro and Maria had fun.
They made new friends.
They helped people.
They plan to do the rally
again next year.

When have you
helped someone?
How did you feel?

Illustrated by Fraser Williamson

Written by Louise Williams

The Race Is On

Photographed by Michael Jacques

A triathlon is a long race.
You do three sports
in a triathlon.

First you swim.
Then you bike.
Then you run.

26

Ready, Set, Swim!

The swimming part
of the race can be
in a swimming pool
or in a river.
It can even be in the ocean.

When you finish swimming,
you run for your bike.

The *tri* in
the word *triathlon*
means *three*.
What words do you know
that start with *tri*?

Ready, Set, Bike!

The biking part
of the race is
long and hard.
You can ride both
on and off the road.

You must drink
lots of water
when you are riding.
If you don't, you will be
too tired to finish.

Many people wear
a swimsuit
for the whole race!

28

Ready, Set, Run!

The running part
of the race is last.

By now you are tired.
But you don't give up.
You run as fast
as you can.
You cross
the finish line.

YOU DID IT!

Have you ever felt
like giving up?

Did you know that triathlons were a medal sport for the first time in the Sydney 2000 Olympic Games?

Index